Stuart Trotter & Sam Walshaw

The Little Bookworm

The little bookworms
favourite treat,
is eating books
sheet by sheet!

Little books, **BIG BOOKS**,
fat books, thin books,
books are starter,
main course, and sweet!

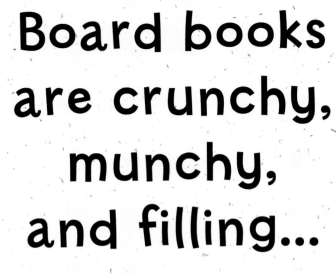

Board books
are crunchy,
munchy,
and filling...

...Pull outs are wholesome,
tender and thrilling!

Picture books are a tasty treat,

Books with sound are scrumptious to eat!

W W W W

Tales of woe
make him
sad and weepy,
and bedtime tales
tired and sleepy!

Buggy books are
for the beginner,
and usually covered
in yesterday's dinner.

Jigsaw books are good to eat, but then, impossible to complete.

Cookery books are
delicious and yummy...

...but pop-up books
upset his tummy!

a is for apple, b is for ball,
c is for cat, d is for...oops,
he's eaten it all!

Add, minus, times, divide,
number books
are nice deep fried.

Finding a place
for the shape to fit,
is hard, when bookworm
has chewed a bit!

Colouring books
are delicious,
with paint and crayon,
quite nutritious.

Furry patches, stuck with glue,
make touchy feelys...

b
is for
bunny

...hard to chew!

Fairy books
that glitter and shine,
are crunchy, munchy,
and divine!

Puzzle books
are rather tricky,
bathbooks chewy,
soapy and sticky.

So when you go to bed
tonight, and say,
"goodnight" to mummy,
you just might hear
a munching sound,
as bookworm fills his tummy...

...and in the morning
there may be left,
as you will plainly see,
a little pile of
paper scraps,
where this book...
used to be!

"Goodbye!"

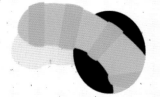

First published in 2015 by Rockpool Children's Books Ltd.

This edition published in 2017 by Rockpool Children's Books
Ltd. in association with Albury Books.
Albury Court, Albury, Thame
OX9 2LP, United Kingdom

Text and Illustrations copyright © Stuart Trotter & Sam Walshaw 2015

Stuart Trotter & Sam Walshaw have asserted the moral rights
to be identified as the authors and illustrators of this book.
© Rockpool Children's Books Ltd. 2015

A CIP catalogue record of this book is available
from the British Library.
Printed in China.

No books
were hurt in
the making

of this...book!

ISBN 978-1-906081-88-1 (Paperback)

rockpool
children's books

Albury Books